Sticker Dolly Dressing
Fashion Designer
New York Collection

Designed and illustrated by Stella Baggott

Additional illustrations by Antonia Miller

Written by Fiona Watt

Contents

How to use this book

These pages will give you some hints and tips about using the stickers to create different outfits for the dolls. They also give you ideas for decorating the pages.

The stickers

If you look at the sticker pages you will see that some of the stickers are blank, some have patterns on them and some are fully colored.

Ideas for colors to use on the stickers

Color in or draw patterns on the plain stickers.

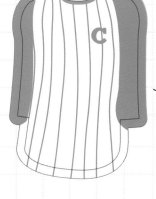

Color in the shapes on the stickers.

Fill the empty space with stickers to make a mood board.

Use the colored stickers just as they are.

Mood boards

Fashion designers often make 'mood boards' to show where they got their ideas for colors, materials and the style of their clothes. Some of the stickers are pictures and photos. Use them to create your own mood boards.

Warning!
The sticker paper is quite smooth, so if you are using felt-tip pens, leave the sticker for a little while before you peel it off. This will give the ink time to dry.

Top Tip
It's a good idea to color in the stickers while they are still on the sticker pages, just in case you go over the edge of the shapes.

Choosing an outfit

Most of the stickers fit all the dolls in the book. They are arranged to match different themes, but you can mix and match them as much as you like. There are extra stickers too, to give you lots of choices for different outfits.

Samples of materials like these are known as 'swatches'.

Complete an outfit with accessories, such as a hat.

You could add details with pens.

Ideas to try

Above are examples of patterns you could use to decorate the plain stickers. There are also more ideas on some of the stickers.

Choose shoes or boots that go with the outfit.

Sightseeing

Use the stickers to dress the dolls for a
day visiting New York's famous buildings,
parks, museums and galleries.

*Fill the space above
with swatches and
photographs from the
sticker pages.*

Ideas for colors to use

On Broadway

Dress the dolls in elegant outfits for the first night of a musical on Broadway. Give them shoes and sparkling accessories to match their dresses.

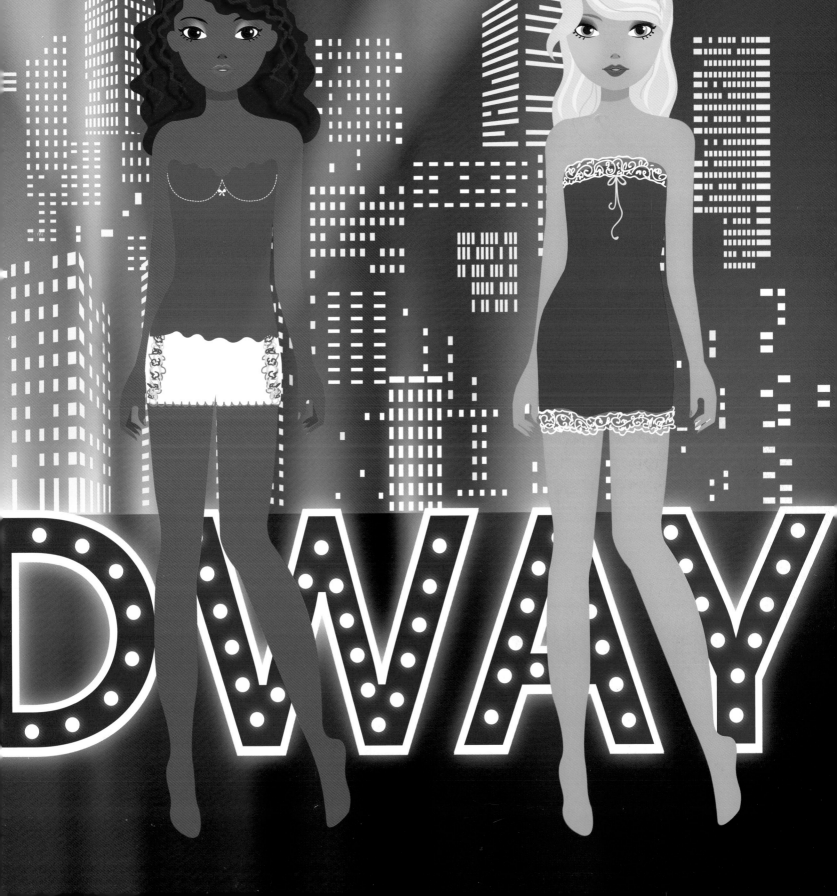

Ideas for colors

DWAY

Sports style

The style and bright colors of sports clothes often influence fashion designers. Dress the dolls in outfits inspired by basketball, baseball and football.

Try using colours like these.

Put the stickers of the sports balls into the spaces above.

Coney Island

The dolls have come to Coney Island for the day to escape the heat and the hustle and bustle of New York City. Dress them in outfits suitable for the rides, attractions and the beach.

Use the stickers to
create a mood board
in the space below.

Ferris wheel

Coney Island beach

Long Island

Use the stickers to create outfits for the dolls for a weekend sailing trip to the beaches on the South Shore of Long Island.

Foodie fashion

You can get just about any kind of food in the world in New York. Even fashion designers are influenced by the huge variety that's found there.

You could color
in the pictures in
the background.

Independence Day

The dolls are watching the spectacular fireworks that light up the night sky over Manhattan every 4th of July.

Create an American-themed moodboard in the space below.

Central Park

There's so much to do in Central Park. Take a dog for a walk, or rollerskate, jog and cycle along the paths around the park.

Society wedding

A lavish wedding ceremony is taking place in a Midtown hotel. Use the stickers to dress the bride and bridesmaids in elegant outfits.

Put the stickers of the lace samples onto the circles above.

Winter in the City

The streets and parks are covered in a deep blanket of snow. Dress the dolls in warm clothes for a walk on a cold winter's day.

You could color in these winter accessories.

Design your own sketchbook

You could start your own sketchbook of fashion designs. Cut out pictures showing where your ideas have come from, or download and print them, then glue them into the book. You could also draw directly onto the pages.

Collect photos and pictures from magazines.

Doodle pictures.

Add pictures showing where you found your color inspiration.

Draw your own swatches or cut out textures from magazines.

Photographs © Thinkstock.

First published in 2016 by Usborne Publishing Ltd., Usborne House , 83-85 Saffron Hill, London, EC1N 8RT, England. www.usborne.com Copyright © 2016 Usborne Publishing Ltd

First published in America 2016. AE

Sightseeing
pages 4-5

7th Avenue

The Statue of Liberty

Put the dolls' shoes on before their dresses.

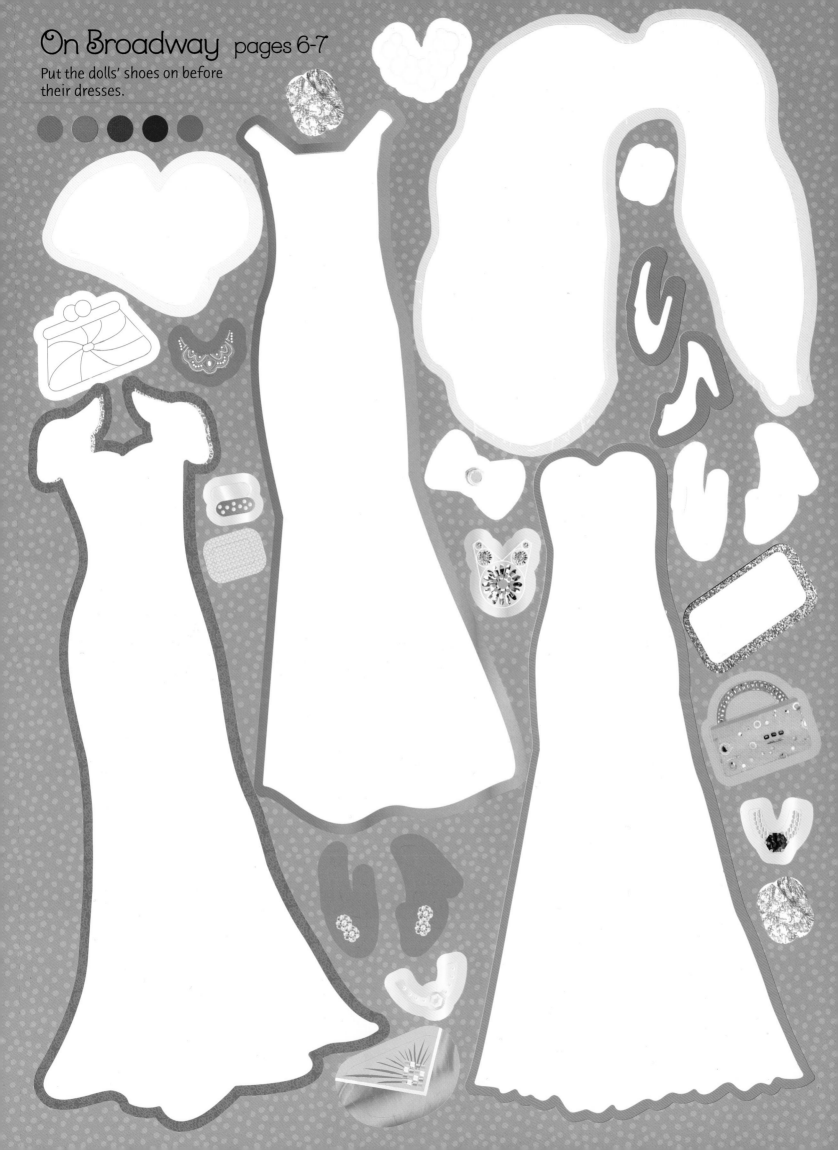

Sports style
pages 8-9

Put the socks on before the
sports shoes.

Long Island
pages 12-13
Put the skirt or bottoms on
before the tops.

Foodie fashion
pages 14-15

Independence Day
pages 16-17

Independence Day muffins

The Statue of Liberty

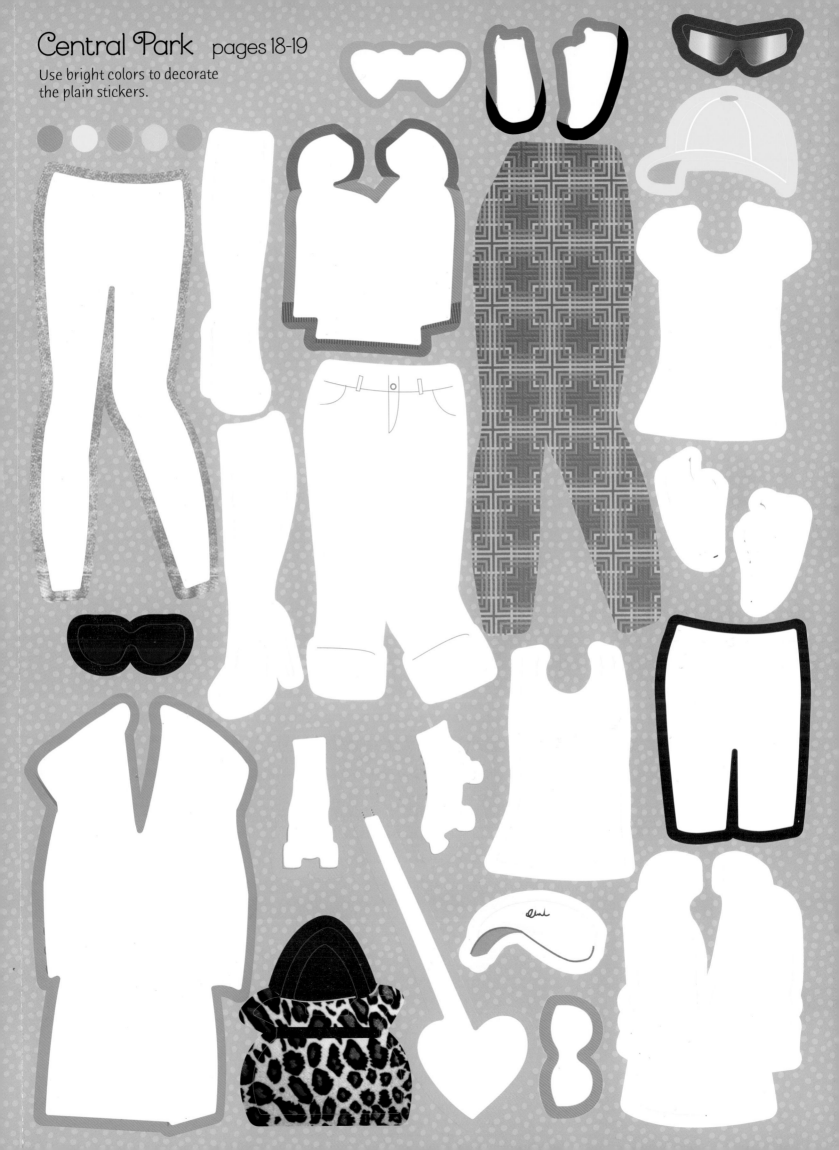

Central Park   pages 18-19

Use bright colors to decorate
the plain stickers.

Put the shoes on before
the dresses.

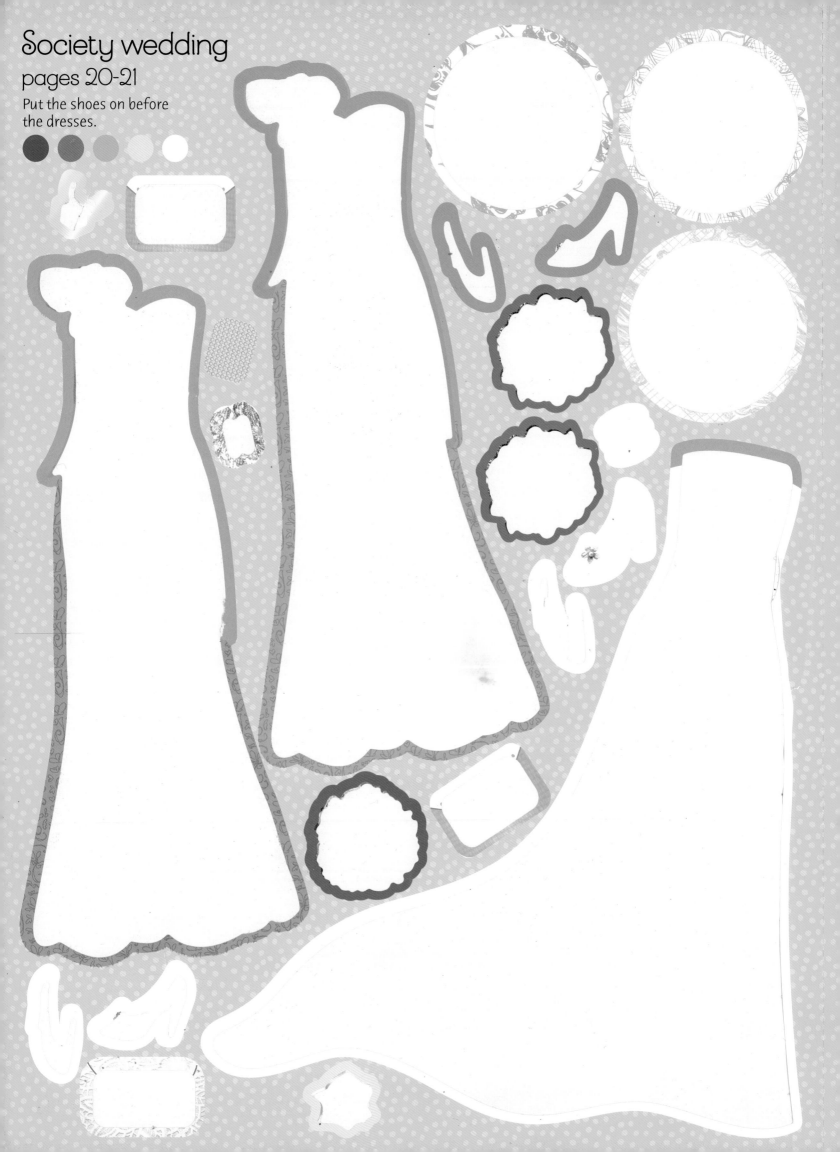